Maths Challenge
Games
Book
LEVEL 3

David Kirkby

WALKER BOOKS
LONDON

Parents' notes

The National Curriculum

AGE   5yrs   12yrs

NATIONAL
CURRICULUM | 1 | 2 | 3 | 4 | 5 |
LEVEL

Mathematics is one of three core subjects within the National Curriculum. The National Curriculum covers the age-range 5–16, and children start at Level 1, with some eventually reaching the top Levels, 8, 9 and 10.

Children will be capable of performing at different levels. For example, a child who is performing mostly at Level 2 will be able to do some activities at Level 3, and perhaps even something at Level 4.

The mathematics curriculum has been divided into 14 areas known as "Attainment Targets" which can be grouped under these headings:
    Using and applying mathematics
    Number
    Algebra
    Measures
    Shape and space
    Data handling

Maths Challenge and the National Curriculum

Maths Challenge is aimed at children within the age-range 5–13 and provides support for children who are already working from Level 1 through to Level 5 at school.

At each Level there are two books – an Activity Book and a Games Book. These are best used in conjunction with each other.

The Activity Book provides mathematical activities across a spectrum of the curriculum, the Games Book contains a collection of mathematical games to consolidate and supplement these ideas.

The contents of the books at each level cover a cross-section of the curriculum. Detailed guides are given to parents relating each activity to particular Attainment Targets within the National Curriculum.

The Maths Challenge series contains:

Activity Books Levels 1 – 5
Games Books Levels 1 – 5

First published 1991 by Walker Books Ltd
87 Vauxhall Walk, London SE11 5HJ
© 1991 David Kirkby   Reprinted 1991
Printed and bound in Hong Kong
by Dai Nippon Printing Co. (HK) Ltd
British Library Cataloguing in Publication Data
A catalogue record for this title is available from
the British Library.
ISBN 0-7445-1886-5

Using the Books

Maths Challenge consolidates the mathematical ideas children have met in school. The ideas are presented here in a lively and stimulating way, to provide an enjoyable learning experience.

Parents can do a lot to support work that their child's school will be covering in mathematics. Do not worry if your child does not pick up the ideas straightaway. Here are some suggestions of ways you can contribute to your child's learning experience through Maths Challenge.

The Activity Books

* Help your child interpret the tasks by talking through the activity with them.
* Ask them to explain some things to you – this is a good way of helping them to learn with more understanding.
* Discourage your child from rushing through the book – one activity per day is sufficient, or even one per week, or when the mood is right.
* Encourage children to do the Challenges – these are an important component of each activity. Sometimes it may be possible to involve other members of the family in these.
* Praise your child frequently for their effort and do not let them worry about making mistakes.

The Games Books

* Help your child interpret the rules.
* All games require two players unless otherwise stated, so here is an opportunity for you to play with your child and observe their mathematical development.
* In some games it may be possible to involve several members of the family.
* Encourage your child to try the Challenges – these often require varying the rules and sometimes gives him or her valuable practice at working alone.
* Discourage children from rushing through the book – it is a good idea to return to the games, particularly those they enjoyed.
* You will need some simple pieces of apparatus:
  2 dice
  a pack of playing cards (Ace counts as 1)
  counters (You can make these from coloured paper. For most games, players must use one colour to avoid confusion.)

Parents' notes

Each activity relates to a combination of different attainment targets outlined in the National Curriculum. These are given in brackets underneath the headings.

1 Stingo

(Number)

"Stingo" provides simple addition practice. Try playing a variation of this game using playing cards numbered 1–10 instead of dice. Deal out the cards in two piles and turn over the top cards for the two numbers. This time the boards will need larger numbers in the squares (from 1–20).

2 Picking mushrooms

(Number)

This game provides simple subtraction practice. If your child enjoyed it why not try taking away from other numbers, for example 11, 9 ...?

3 Multiplication

(Number)

This game practises multiplication up to the 6 x table. It may be helpful to draw a 6 x 6 multiplication table before you start. If your child needs further practice try pointing to different numbers on the board and asking which dice numbers will multiply together to make that number. For example, 20 – answer 4 and 5.

4 Target

(Number)

Play a variation in which players score points according to the difference between their written numbers and the target.

5 Satellites

(Number)

This game practises counting and adding on to the running total. Vary the game by changing the target from 30 to other numbers.

6 Number match

(Number, Algebra, Shape and space)

Another game combining addition and subtraction practice. A starting point for this game may be simply to take it in turns to pick up a card from the pile and place a counter on the correct hexagon.

7 Sea lions

(Handling data, Number; Using and applying)

The purpose of this game is to provide the child with an intuitive feel for the chances associated with each rule. A variation would be to change the number of dice throws.

8 Boxes

(Number, Shape and space)

In this game children may need help with adding up the total scores at the end – they could be encouraged to use a calculator to help them.

9 Differences

(Number)

This game requires players to find pairs of numbers for a given difference. Similar practice can be had by using a pack of cards instead of a dice.

10 Bridge

(Number)

This simple game practises addition skills. Play it regularly whilst skills are improving.

11 Side race

(Number, Algebra, Shape and space)

This game gives children a chance to recognize different polygons and to learn their names. Ask your child to make his or her own "Side race" board.

12 Six sums

(Number)

A good game to practise both addition and subtraction together. Devise some different but similar game cards, but make sure that the boxes can be filled by numbers in the range 1 – 9. The Challenge is something you could do together and help to check your child's arithmetic.

13 Cover-up

(Shape and space)

This should give your child experience in visualizing in two-dimensional space. If you think your child is confident why not play a harder variation of the game with L–shaped pieces instead of rectangles?

14 Noughts and crosses

(Number, Shape and space)

To save having to draw grids you could make a large 5 x 5 board and use counters of two colours instead of Os and Xs.

11	5	2	6
3	9	3	1
4	5	2	10
4	12	7	8

You will need:
2 dice
16 counters each

This is a game for 2–4 players. Each player chooses a board. Take turns to throw the two dice. You can place a counter on one of the numbers on the board that either matches one of the dice numbers or the SUM of the dice numbers. If, for example, you throw

then you can place a counter on **5**
or **3**
or **8 (5+3)**.
The winner is the first player to cover his/her board.

3	5	10	5
11	7	2	3
4	6	9	12
8	1	6	4

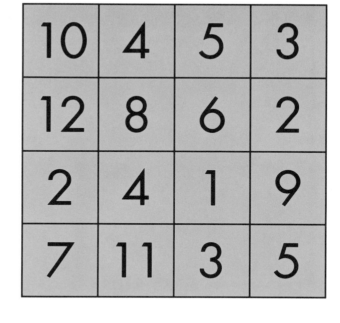

10	4	5	3
12	8	6	2
2	4	1	9
7	11	3	5

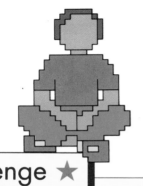

★ Challenge ★

You can design your own boards by writing your choice of numbers in the squares.

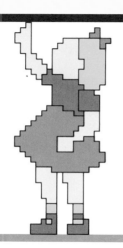

8	5	12	2
5	1	3	7
4	9	6	11
10	4	3	2

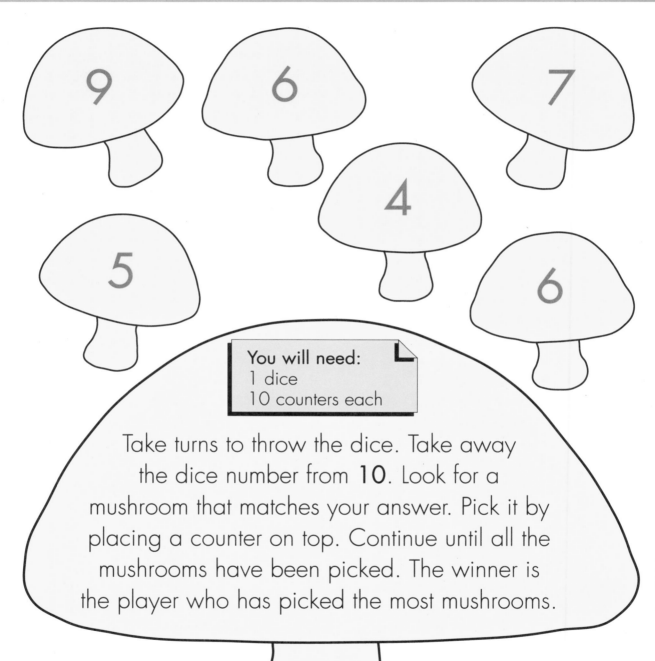

9

6

7

4

5

6

You will need:
1 dice
10 counters each

Take turns to throw the dice. Take away
the dice number from **10**. Look for a
mushroom that matches your answer. Pick it by
placing a counter on top. Continue until all the
mushrooms have been picked. The winner is
the player who has picked the most mushrooms.

★ **Challenge** ★

Play by yourself and see how many throws you need to pick 10 mushrooms.

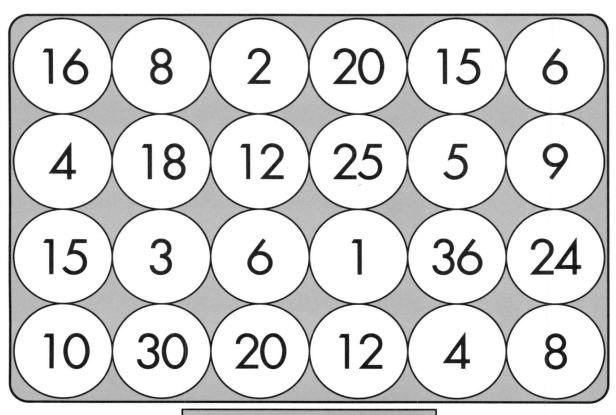

GREEN BOARD

You will need:
2 dice
20 counters each

Each player chooses a board. Take turns to throw the two dice and MULTIPLY the numbers together. If a circle on your board contains the result, then place a counter on that circle.

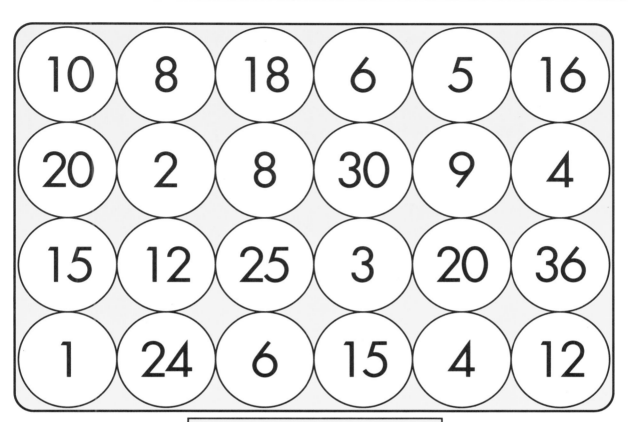

10	8	18	6	5	16
20	2	8	30	9	4
15	12	25	3	20	36
1	24	6	15	4	12

YELLOW BOARD

The winner is the first player to make a vertical line of four counters.

★ **Challenge** ★

Play by yourself and see how many throws you need to make a horizontal line of six counters.

You will need: 2 dice, pencil

Write your names above a column in the Game Card. Take turns to throw two dice. Use the result to write a two-digit number on the card.

EXAMPLE: John's throw

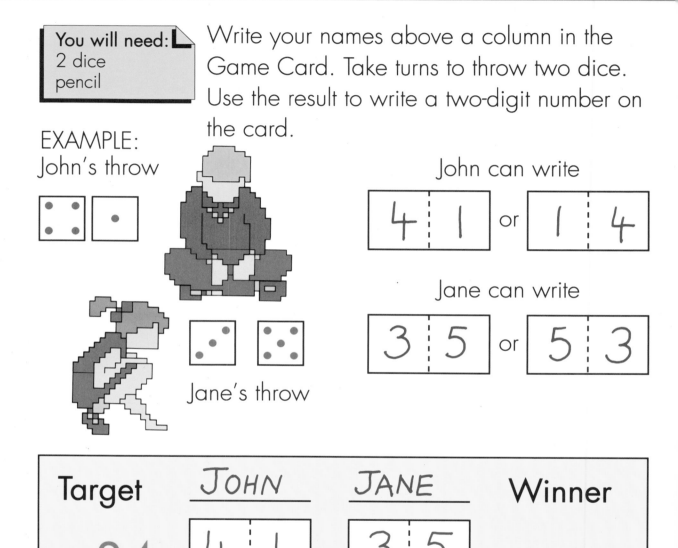

John can write

| 4 | 1 | or | 1 | 4 |

Jane can write

| 3 | 5 | or | 5 | 3 |

Jane's throw

Target	JOHN	JANE	Winner
1. 34	4 1	3 5	JANE

The player whose number is nearest to the TARGET wins the round.

TARGET GAME CARD

Target			Winner
1. **34**			
2. **53**			
3. **16**			
4. **25**			
5. **42**			

★ Challenge ★

Devise another game card with different targets and play again.

5 Satellites

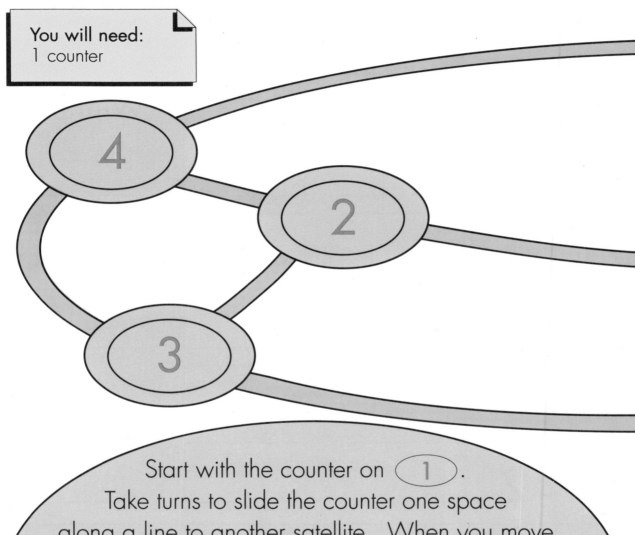

Start with the counter on ① .
Take turns to slide the counter one space
along a line to another satellite. When you move
you say the RUNNING TOTAL. For example, if the first
player slides from ① to ④ he says "5"; if the
next player slides to ② she says "7", and so on.
The winner is the first player
to say "30" or more.

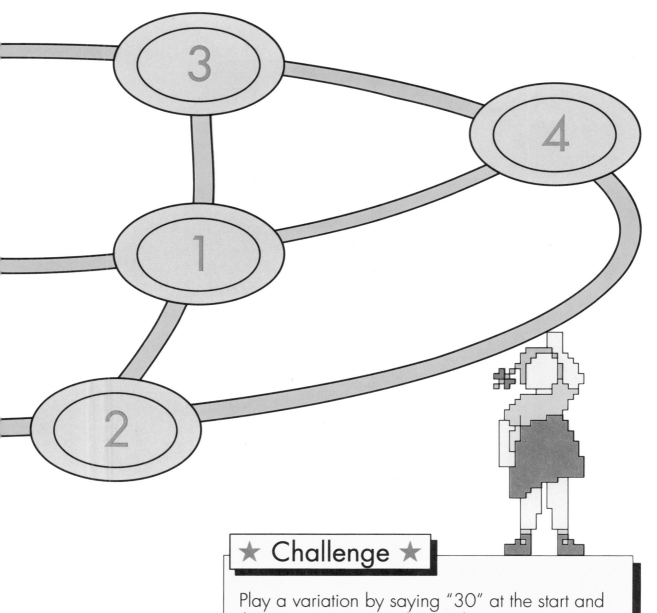

★ Challenge ★

Play a variation by saying "30" at the start and
then SUBTRACTING the numbers as you move.
The winner is the first player to reach "0".

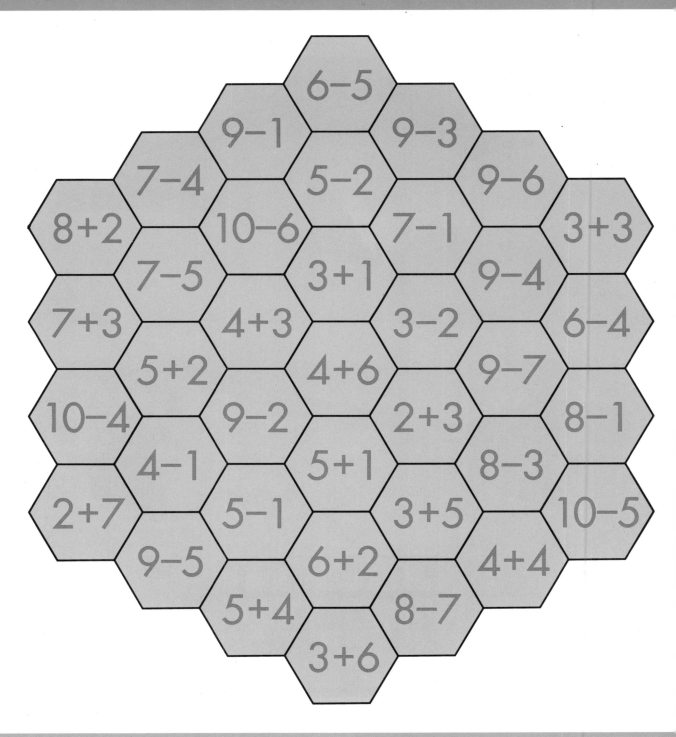

You will need:
a pack of playing cards
20 counters each

Use all the cards numbered 1–10. Shuffle the cards and deal ten to each player. Put the remaining cards in a pile, face down.

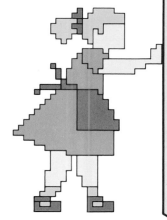

Look at the cards in your hand. Take turns to put down a card whose number matches the sum on one of the hexagons. Place a counter on that hexagon and pick up another card from the top of the pile. The winner is the first player to make a straight line of 4 counters on joined hexagons.

★ Challenge ★

Why not play a variation? Shuffle the cards and place them all in a pile face down. Take turns to remove the top card and attempt to place a counter. The first player to make a straight line of 4 wins.

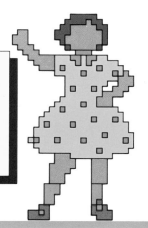

You will need:
1 dice
12 counters

GAME 1

The aim of the game is to give the sea lions balls to balance on their heads. One player throws the dice 12 times and the other places the counters according to the rules. Before each round both players guess how many balls each sea lion will have to balance. The winner is the player whose guess is the nearest after 12 throws.

If the dice number is ODD place a ball on this sea lion

If the dice number is EVEN place a ball on this sea lion

ODD NUMBER

EVEN NUMBER

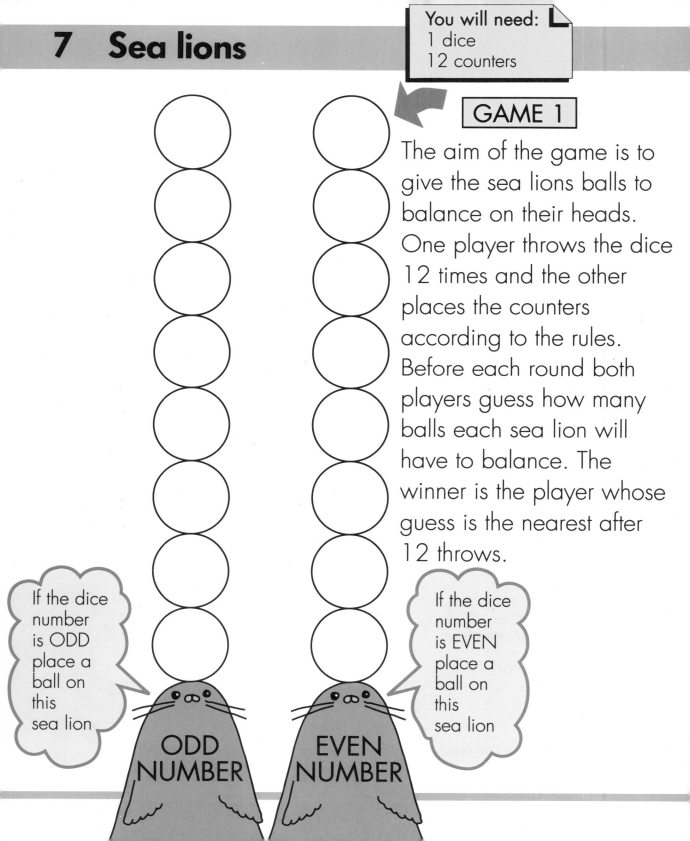

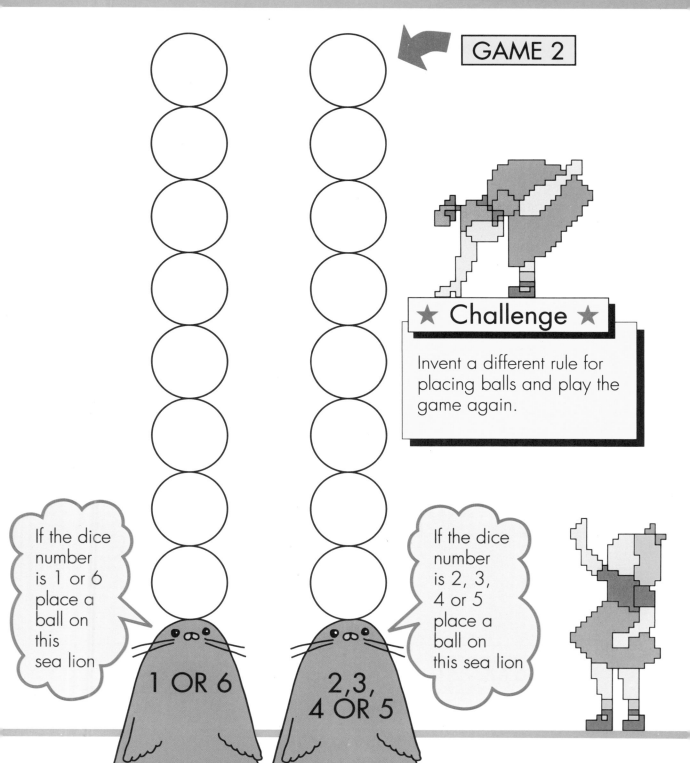

GAME 2

★ Challenge ★

Invent a different rule for placing balls and play the game again.

If the dice number is 1 or 6 place a ball on this sea lion

1 OR 6

If the dice number is 2, 3, 4 or 5 place a ball on this sea lion

2,3, 4 OR 5

You will need:
2 different coloured pencils
a scoresheet

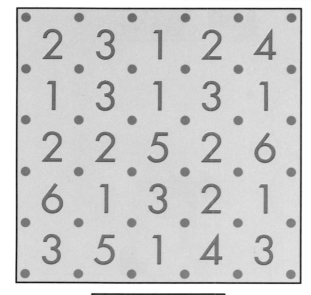

```
2 3 1 2 4
1 3 1 3 1
2 2 5 2 6
6 1 3 2 1
3 5 1 4 3
```

GAME 1

```
1 2 4 3 1
3 1 0 2 4
2 4 1 3 5
1 3 2 0 4
4 1 5 3 2
```

GAME 2

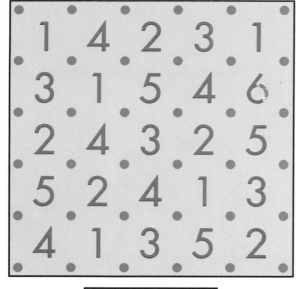

```
1 4 2 3 1
3 1 5 4 6
2 4 3 2 5
5 2 4 1 3
4 1 3 5 2
```

GAME 3

```
5 4 3 2 1
4 3 2 1 0
3 5 4 1 2
2 3 1 5 4
0 1 2 3 4
```

GAME 4

Each player chooses a different coloured pencil. Take turns to draw a straight line, horizontally or vertically, joining two dots next to each other.

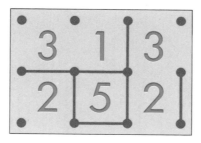

When your lines complete a small square then you score points equal to the number inside and have another turn.

SCORE
5 POINTS

When all the squares have been completed add up the points. The winner is the person with the highest score.

★ Challenge ★

Design your own Boxes game boards.
Each player starts with 50 points. When a box is completed the number is SUBTRACTED from your total.
The winner is the player with the lowest score at the end.

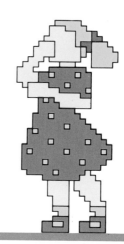

9 Differences

You will need:
1 dice
20 counters each

Each player chooses a board.
Take turns to throw the dice.
Place two counters on numbers whose DIFFERENCE
matches the DICE NUMBER.
The first player unable to place a counter loses.

EXAMPLE: If you throw  place counters on two numbers which have a difference of 3.

⑧ and ⑪ or ② and ⑤

10 Bridge

You will need:
a pack of playing cards
20 counters each

Use all the cards numbered 1–10.
Shuffle them and deal out three piles,
face up.

Take turns to choose two cards whose TOTAL matches a bridge number. Remove the cards and place a counter on the bridge number. The first player unable to place a counter loses.

★ Challenge ★

Play by yourself. See how many counters you can place before you can't go.

4	16	5	8
11	18	9	7
	6	7	14
	13	16	3

You will need:
1 dice
1 counter each

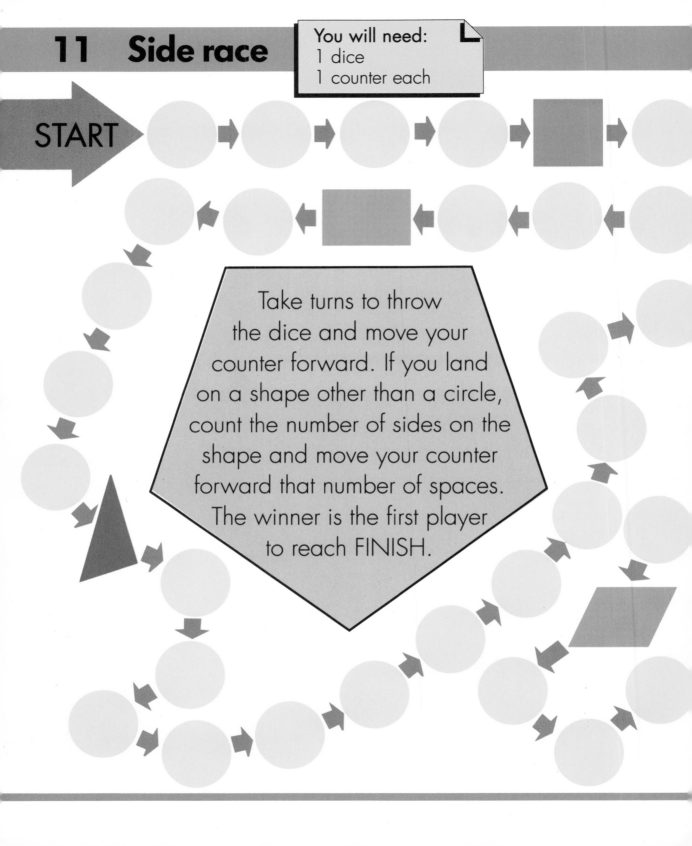

START

Take turns to throw the dice and move your counter forward. If you land on a shape other than a circle, count the number of sides on the shape and move your counter forward that number of spaces. The winner is the first player to reach FINISH.

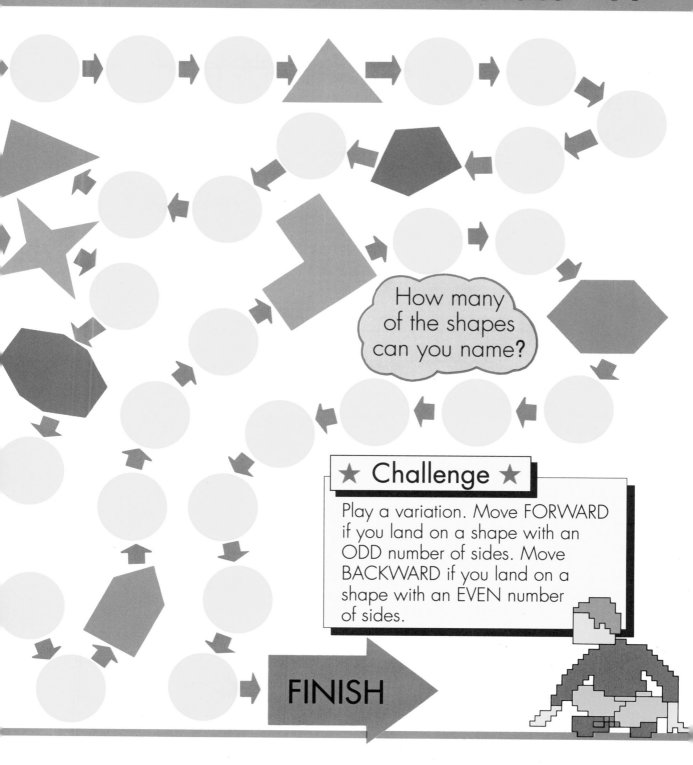

How many of the shapes can you name?

★ Challenge ★

Play a variation. Move FORWARD if you land on a shape with an ODD number of sides. Move BACKWARD if you land on a shape with an EVEN number of sides.

FINISH

SIX SUMS GAME CARD

$$\square + \square = 9$$

$$\begin{array}{c} \square \\ + \square \\ \hline 8 \end{array} \qquad \begin{array}{c} \square \\ - \square \\ \hline 3 \end{array} \qquad \begin{array}{c} \square \\ + \square \\ \hline 12 \end{array}$$

$$\square + \square - \square = 4$$

$$\square - \square = 5$$

You will need:
a pack of playing cards
pencils and paper

This game can be played by any number of people.

Each player copies the Game Card.

Use all the cards numbered 1–9.

Shuffle the cards and place them in a pile, face down.

One player turns over the top card.

All players can choose to write the number in one of
the boxes on the sheet or ignore it.

Then turn over the next card, and so on.

The winner is the first player to complete all the boxes correctly.

★ Challenge ★

On your own, shuffle the cards and deal out
thirteen, face up.

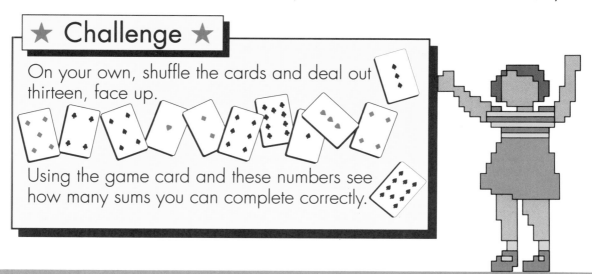

Using the game card and these numbers see
how many sums you can complete correctly.

You will need:
paper or card
scissors

Trace and cut out
8 RECTANGLES
this size from card.

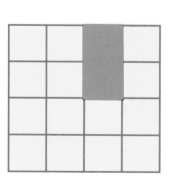

Take turns to place a rectangle
on the board, covering two squares.

The first player who can't go loses.

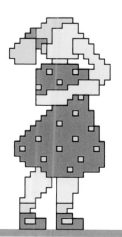

★ Challenge ★

Make a larger board (5 x 5 or 6 x 6),
cut out a few more rectangles and
play some more games.

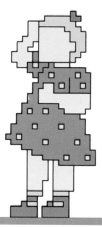

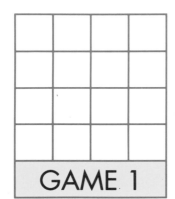

GAME 1

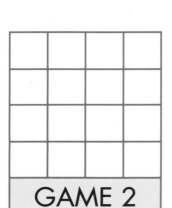

GAME 2

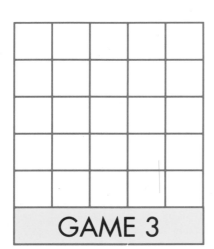

GAME 3

One player uses Os, the other Xs.
Take turns to put your mark in a square.
When the grid is complete you score:
3 points for each line of three.
4 points for each line of four.

EXAMPLE:

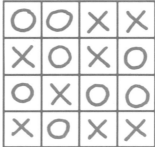

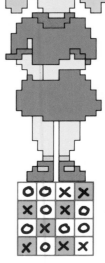

X has one line of three
and one line of four
= 7 points
O has two lines of three
= 6 points
X wins

★ Challenge ★

Play on a 6 x 6 square and score
5 points for each line of five.